Shivers

Tales from *The Book of Darkness & Light*

by Adam Z. Robinson

Stories
The New Priest of Blackpines
Dead Air
A Horror in Porcelain

Shivers is a co-production between The Book of Darkness & Light, Harrogate Theatres, Square Chapel Arts Centre and LittleMighty.

Published by Playdead Press 2018

© Adam Z. Robinson 2018

Adam Z. Robinson has asserted his rights under the Copyright, Design and Patents Act, 1988, to be identified as the author of this work.

A CIP catalogue record for this book is available from the British Library.

ISBN 978-1-910067-70-3

Playdead Press
www.playdeadpress.com

Cover design: Wayne Gamble
Photography: Barnaby Aldrick

For Jane and Martin

CAST & CREATIVE TEAM

Adam Z. Robinson | Writer and 'The Storyteller'

Ben Styles | Composer and 'The Musician'

Dick Bonham | Dramaturg

Aly Howe | Technical Stage Manager

LittleMighty | Producer

ADAM Z. ROBINSON | WRITER AND THE STORYTELLER

Adam Z. Robinson is a storyteller and a writer of theatre, short fiction and film. His play *The Book of Darkness & Light* toured nationally in both 2016 and 2017 to more than 50 theatres, arts spaces and libraries. He was one of the commissioned writers for Andy Craven-Griffiths' *Joygernaut* project in 2018, alongside Inua Elams, Vanessa Kisuule and Byron Vincent. His short film for the project, *Quiet Coach*, starred Nick Fawcett (*Perfect Place, Doctors*) and was co-directed by Nick Coupe (producer BBC Radio 4's *News Quiz Extra, Newsjack*). Adam co-wrote *Seaside Terror* with Odd Doll Puppetry, which toured in autumn 2017. He was one of the writers on Common Chorus's *A Wind of Change* which premiered in 2018. Adam's short film *The Split* was directed by Ed Rigg (*Confection, Passenger*) and starred Edward Hogg (*Taboo, Indian Summers*). It has screened at several international film festivals including the Manchester Film Festival, Berlin's 'British Shorts' festival, the Cambridge Film Festival and the London Short Film Festival. Adam co-wrote and co-directed the short film *Go On, My Son* (with Nick Coupe), which was supported by Roundhouse, London. Adam's play *Conscientious* toured nationally in 2014. The show was directed by Alex Chisholm and performed by Rachel Ashwanden. He is the author of *Bad House* (NSDF 2010 - co-written with Lucy Arnold) and *Little Red* (Edinburgh Fringe 2008). He is currently working on a new piece of theatre with Andrea Heaton called *Smile Club* and a new storytelling show called *This Storm is What We Call Progress.*

BEN STYLES | COMPOSER AND THE MUSICIAN

Ben Styles is a musician and composer, publishing editor and software developer. He has been playing music since the age of 7. While at university, he found a violin in a friend's attic and set himself the challenge of teaching himself to play it. Within a year he had joined a band, **Backyards**. The band played the BBC Introducing stages at Leeds and Reading Festival. They had several releases, including *If You're Scared*, *Underbank Hall* and *Goodhart's Law*. *The Book of Darkness & Light* was Ben's first theatre project and he collaborated with Adam again on *Shivers.*

DICK BONHAM | DRAMATURG

Dick Bonham is an experienced director, dramaturg and producer. His most recent play was *If I Say Jump* for Common Chorus Theatre ("fast-moving, funny and very entertaining" - British Theatre Guide). As a director he has an ongoing partnership with Daniel Bye, recently directing the Fringe First Award winning *Going Viral*, as well as previous pieces *The Price of Everything* and *How to Occupy An Oil Rig*. Other projects include Matthew Bellwood's *An Icy Man*, which premiered at the West Yorkshire Playhouse, and Emma Decent's *Beyond Dreams of Aberystwyth* (The Lowry, Salford Quays and touring). He wrote and directed *We Can Be Heroes*, which toured nationally in 2015. He is currently developing his own show, *Thinner Blood*, which will premiere in 2019

ALY HOWE | TECHNICAL STAGE MANAGER

Aly Howe is a Technician and Stage Manager who works across a number of disciplines and backstage roles. Stage Management credits include productions with Red Ladder Theatre Company: *Big Society* (DSM 2012), *The Damned United* (DSM 2017 Tour) and *Mother Courage and Her Children* (CSM 2018). She works as a TSM and Lighting Designer touring with a number of LittleMighty associate companies such as Luna Bug, Odd Doll, Most Wanted,

Sometimes We Play, as well as various other performers and theatre makers in and around the North of England. She is delighted to collaborate with The TBODAL team once again on their 2018-19 tour of *Shivers.*

LITTLEMIGHTY | PRODUCER
LittleMighty is an independent producer based in Leeds that works nationally with remarkable artists to make brilliant theatre happen. Their recent successes include Silent Uproar's multi-award winning *A Super Happy Story (About Feeling Super Sad)* at the Edinburgh Fringe; Unfolding Theatre's *Putting the Band Back Together* (Journal Culture Awards: Best Performance); and Testament's *WOKE* (co-production with Leeds Playhouse, The Royal Exchange Manchester, The Roundhouse and CPT).
www.littlemighty.co.uk

SQUARE CHAPEL ARTS CENTRE | CO-COMMISSIONER
Square Chapel is an arts centre in the heart of Halifax (West Yorkshire) and the beating, red brick heart of a remarkable cultural quarter for the town. Providing a unique platform for a diverse range of high quality live performance, events and film, alongside talent development for emerging artists and creatives and an extensive community outreach and education programme, Square Chapel Arts Centre is a vibrant hub for culture, community and creativity. Once a receiving house exclusively, in 2017, along with the opening of its stunning new building, Square Chapel began producing and co-producing new work and adaptations. Credits include Andrea Dunbar's *Shirley* (2017), Adam Z. Robinson's *Shivers* (2017), Lucy Kirkwood & Katie Mitchell's *Beauty and the Beast* (2017), Guild of Misrule & Theatr Clwyd's *The Great Gatsby* (after F. Scott Fitzgerald) (2018), Knaïve Theatre's

War With the Newts (after Karel Čapek) (2018) and Debs Newbold's *Outrageous Fortune* (2019).

HARROGATE THEATRE | CO-COMMISSIONER
Harrogate Theatre was built in 1900 and is located in central Harrogate. It has two performance spaces (one mid-scale and one studio), which allow for producing and presenting theatre, dance, music and comedy. The organisation runs a vibrant education and outreach department that delivers throughout the District. In addition, Harrogate Theatre Scenic Services, operated by Harrogate Theatre, builds sets for companies all over the country including Sheffield Theatres, Opera North, Hampstead Theatre amongst many others. The Theatre has undergone considerable artistic development in the past 10 years that has seen the organisation establish itself as a significant influence in the region, with a growing national profile. As well as producing an annual pantomime and a repertory company, the theatre supports artists to make their own work. Recent supported artists include **Adam Z. Robinson**, **1927 Productions**, **Kill the Beast**, **Fidget Theatre** and **Square Peg Theatre**.

"This theatre is doing more than punching above its weight, it has adopted a striking new profile." – The Stage

THE BOOK OF DARKNESS & LIGHT

The Book of Darkness & Light was created by writer Adam Z. Robinson and musician Ben Styles. Originally conceived for Light Night Leeds in 2015, the premise was simple: original, gothic tales told live to the sounds of the violin. At that first event, over 1,500 people came to see and listen to a ghost story told in the beautiful, atmospheric surroundings of Leeds's oldest church.

Afterwards, Adam and Ben went on to create a 'Ghost Stories for Christmas' show which played two sell-out performances at the Hyde Park Book Club, Leeds. In June 2016, the show received funding from Arts Council England for a tour in autumn/winter of that year, visiting libraries, theatres and arts spaces. The show received further support from Arts Council England to play at 23 theatres on their 2017 national tour.

Shivers, the follow-up to *The Book of Darkness & Light*, was developed in association with Square Chapel Arts Centre, Harrogate Theatres and LittleMighty. The show premiered in September 2017 at Square Chapel before a run of four performances at Harrogate Theatre in January 2018. The show toured from October 2018 to February 2019, playing at 33 venues across more than 40 performances. This tour was supported using public funding by Arts Council England, receiving a National Lottery Project grant.

The third instalment of *The Book of Darkness & Light* is currently in production. Join our mailing list for updates...

www.thebookofdarknessandlight.com

NOTE FROM THE AUTHOR

There's an old theory that the horror genre holds up a mirror to society. That each novel, short story, film and play reflects and reacts to what's happening in the world at the precise moment in which it was created. The tales in *Shivers* are shot-through with the themes of isolationism, ubiquitous fear and selfishness. The play includes a story of a community cut off from the rest of the world in an attempt to preserve the 'old ways'; a confession of a man who lives with daily, lonesome anxiety and a constant, lurking terror of communication; a tale of an authority figure who obeys his reactionary gut rather than his rational brain. Perhaps the old theory is true.

When I first read an early version of *Shivers* to our dramaturg and producer, Dick Bonham, he said, 'Wow. These stories are a lot more "horror" than the last show!' Making *Shivers* a scarier, more horror-inflected thing wasn't intentional - it happened organically. All Ben Styles and I knew was that the play needed to be bigger and bolder than *The Book of Darkness & Light,* whilst still maintaining the creeping, intimate charm we tried to create with that first collection of tales. A tricky and exciting challenge.

When I approached Square Chapel Arts Centre and Harrogate Theatre with the idea of a follow up to *TBODAL*, I didn't know what the response would be. We were a young company and we were asking them to take a chance on something without knowing what the outcome might be. Both theatres got onboard immediately and gave us complete freedom to make the show we wanted to make. Without the two theatres, *Shivers* probably wouldn't have happened at all. I'm so grateful to them for saying 'yes'!

As for the stories: I'd had the initial idea for *The New Priest of Blackpines* when spending Christmas in Germany in 2013. My partner and I spent a lot of time in Bavaria and the Black Forest. Those magical places ignited my Gothic imagination. I threw down some ideas about a haunted wood and left them to fester in an old notebook. A few years later, I happened to read a news story about an 8th-century skeleton that had been discovered in Ireland, buried with a rock wedged in its mouth. At roughly the same time, I heard a podcast which detailed some research on the proliferation of black mould in reportedly haunted houses. These three elements, somehow, came together to create the spine of the tale. In the writing period, I went back to my notes and an idea of a sole stranger visiting an isolated community in order to offer (unwanted, un-asked for) help started to emerge. I had the image of Blackpines forest in my head from very early on and the scene in which Reverend Hoffman bursts through the door after being attacked by the 'dead thing' in the woods was, I think, the very first image I came up with for *Shivers*. I hope the loving allusions to *The Wicker Man*, *The Blair Witch Project* and *The Devil Rides Out* are evident in this story, even if they're only creeping around in the trees. *The New Priest of Blackpines* is our contribution to the Folk Horror revival.

With *Dead Air*, the plan was to do something totally different to anything we'd written before. Something more challenging and contemporary. Something, actually, that didn't feel like a segment of one of our shows at all. We also needed a bridging story. The middle section of a three-part portmanteau show has to do a tricky thing. It has to be both a palate-cleanser and a gear-change. It shouldn't follow the same rules or have the same atmosphere as the first and third stories. In our first show, *Girl, Dancing* is a much sadder, more melancholy and poetic story, which feels closer to fairy tale than ghost story. I wrote it quickly (years before *TBODAL* existed) and it hasn't really changed very much since its first incarnation as part of my and artist Max Dorey's blog, *Tales from the Red Barn*. Similarly, of all of the stories in *Shivers*, *Dead Air* is the one that is most similar to its very first draft. Both words and music came together quickly, which made me a little suspicious (even superstitious?). I remember, on the week of the premiere performance at Square Chapel, turning to Ben and saying, 'I can't tell if this one is terrible or not.' I wasn't being self-deprecating. I meant it. It was (and is) such a departure in more or less every way. It's got a high-camp drama to it that the other stories we've done don't have. It has moments of lightness and comedy which could have jarred with the tone of the whole play. It has – crucially – another character in it (played brilliantly by Ali Ford). It is also, without question, the story which most people tell us is their favourite in *Shivers*. It shows how you never know what will work until you try it in front of a room full of people. That, in itself, is terrifying but I'm so glad we took the risk. It's my favourite section to perform.

I think *A Horror in Porcelain* is my favourite story of the three. I remember being determined to try something different with the well-trodden 'haunted doll' trope. Something fresh and original and scary. The first bit of writing I did on the story was the 'Barlow's Birth' section. That short moment is inspired by Goya's black paintings (specifically, *Aquelarre/El Gran Cabrón*) and the story began to form from there. Like *Blackpines,* it draws upon the tradition of folk horror and, similarly to *The Bonehouse* in our first show, it has a villain at the centre. Initially, the character of Delaney (originally called Carmichael, for reasons I've forgotten) was going to be more prominent. A Trumpian figure whose politics reflected the ugliest elements of today's society. But as drafts went on, I became a lot more interested in Williams and the journey to collect the doll. The moment with the 'moving' doll in Delaney's lounge ('THERE!') was another early image that I wanted to realise on stage. I wondered if we could create a tense, almost cinematic moment in which we could convince an audience that they had seen something happen on stage when, in fact, it hadn't. I don't know if that's what we achieve, but I can always feel the tension in the room at that moment and it is thrilling for me every single time.

At that first reading of *Shivers* with Dick Bonham, he also said, 'If your first show was Hammer, this one is Amicus'. Fans of classic horror will appreciate the subtle differences between those two studios and their fantastical, bloody output. We'll certainly take that comparison and hope it's one you find in the show. *Shivers* is an absolute joy to perform and I'm grateful for every opportunity to do so. I really hope you enjoy seeing it and, now, reading it. We'll see you for the next instalment of *The Book of Darkness & Light*.

Adam Z. Robinson
September 2018

THANK YOU

I'd sincerely like to thank the following...

Ben Styles, who has been my partner in this from the beginning. It's always an absolute pleasure to write and perform with him, and to hear the incredible music he composes. Anna Wiseman for everything she does for me, for always encouraging me to keep going, no matter what the challenges, and for always pointing out the lights in the darkness. Danielle Parkinson for her enormous support of Ben, and of this project. Aly Howe, our incredible technical stage manager, jelly road driver, car raconteur and third part of the TBODAL triptych – *shells forever*! Everyone at Square Chapel Arts Centre and everyone at Harrogate Theatres for allowing us to get *Shivers* off the ground in first place. Without their support, this wouldn't have happened at all. Ali Ford and Emma McDowell, for being so supportive and enthusiastic about *Shivers* from the beginning, and for being big parts in allowing us to make the show. Rachel Ashwanden for her vocal work in *A Horror in Porcelain* in the premiere performances. Ali Ford, Amy Marchant and Edmund Digby-Jones for their wonderful vocal performances in the tales for the 2018-19 tour. Sam Mitchell for his lighting and technical design on the original performance in Halifax, and for being a vital part of the *Shivers* team during development. Dick Bonham for brilliant dramaturgy and direction – he's been an essential factor in bringing the stories to life. Emma Williams for her creative design brilliance. Mike Muncer for inviting me on to The Evolution of Horror podcast to talk about *Shivers* and FrightFest. Rosie Fletcher at Den of Geek for her support of Shivers. Penny Dreadful for the inclusion in her SFX column. Thom Burgess for constant support and kind words about our shows. Everyone at Slung Low's HUB for giving us a home during rehearsals. Jane and Martin Wiseman (to whom this book is dedicated) for giving me an actual home for most of 2018 and providing me with a wonderful writing eyrie in their attic. Heather and Peter for putting us up and putting up with us (again) in Lancaster. Rose and Laura for spreading the word brilliantly in Bournemouth. Dr Sarah Burnett for her medical expertise when I was writing *The New Priest of Blackpines* – even if I did take some huge creative liberties and pronounce things incorrectly. Nick Coupe and Andrew Dobbie for being the first readers of the tales and for always knowing how to make them better. Andy Craven-Griffiths, my friend and confidant on writing, philosophy and more or less everything else. Proofreaders Becky Darke, Cathy Neligan and Laura Price who did an amazing job at spotting my clumsy mistakes. Our Street Team and Facebook, Instagram and Twitter friends and followers - we're so grateful for every gesture of support. All of our friends in the many theatres and venues we've visited. Arts Council England for supporting our work and allowing us to make and tour more of it. Jon Hudson and Steve Watling, our two new technical stage managers on the 2018-19 tour. Lauren Lister, our BSL interpreter for the 2018-19 tour. Jon Foxley-Evans and Chris Bromley for another outstanding trailer - it's always a pleasure to work with them. Temple Newsam in Leeds for providing an amazingly atmospheric location for the trailer. Wayne Gamble for yet more incredible design on the book, the posters and the flyers. Elliot Robinson and our publishers, Playdead Press. Our producers, LittleMighty, who've worked so hard this year to help us bring the show to over thirty theatres. My parents, my family, my friends. All of our audiences, past and future. Thank you!

A NOTE ON PERFORMANCE

In the original production of *Shivers*, The Storyteller maintained a single, unique persona for each story - i.e. the narrator of each tale. There are, however, several other character voices throughout the tales which can be presented as audio recordings (as in the original production). Alternatively, The Storyteller can perform these parts him/herself, or the play can be performed as an ensemble.

At the time of publishing, *Shivers* was still in rehearsal. As such, there may be elements of the performed version of the play which differ from the script as it appears, here.

CHARACTERS

On Stage
THE STORYTELLER
THE MUSICIAN

In The Tales
REV. MICHAEL HOFFMAN
ABIGAIL HOFFMAN
MR PALFREMAN
BLACKPINES HISTORIAN
ALICE
DAVID
WILLIAMS
DELANEY
DOROTHY
BARLOW EXPERT
WINSTANLEY
BETTY BEAUCHAMP

PROLOGUE

Set: Downstage, left is an old chair. A side-table on which a single candle flickers. A decanter of brandy with a full glass. A collection of suitcases, trunks, boxes all bursting with hand-written papers, photographs and printed documents. Upstage, right: another collection of boxes and cases; the musician stands just beyond this, further upstage but not obscured.

Darkness.

A thunderstorm.

Slowly, the sound of Latin whispers creeps in. It rises to a crescendo. A sudden scream and the light snaps on.

The Storyteller and **The Musician** appear.

STORYTELLER: Condemned. We are condemned.

For more years than I care to count, we have been walking the land with this...

Produces The Book of Darkness & Light. It is ancient, tattered, ominous.

This book of darkness and light.

From the darkest forests of Bavaria, to the alleyways of the souks of Marrakech to the frozen wastes of Siberia to... this place.

Mercy.

Who we are... is of no consequence. How the book came to be in our possession... we will come to when the time is right.

What matters is the task with which we are charged.

The Book of Darkness and Light contains within it some of the most chilling tales ever recorded. And we are sentenced to carry it. And to share from its pages.

The punishment for breaking our pact is beyond any horror you can imagine. And so, we walk. And we share. There are lessons in these tales for those who would heed them.

Tonight, we bring you three unquiet tales.

But I warn you, before we proceed, that these stories are not for the faint of heart. And you are not bound to this, as we are. We offer you a final opportunity... to back out. To defy your curiosity. To escape.

House lights lift slightly on the audience.

A single thread of music plays.

After a moment, when nobody leaves, the house lights come back down.

Very well. We begin...

ACT 1

THE NEW PRIEST OF BLACKPINES

NEW PRIEST theme

1.

STORYTELLER: Our first story concerns the remote North Sea isle of Shorehollow; and more specifically, its only inhabited township: the village of Blackpines.

Two months ago - drawn by the story I am about to tell you - I found myself standing in the Blackpines Library, face-to-face with a most ungodly sight.

In a dingy back room of the old building is a modest collection of exhibits relating to the history of the village.

The centrepiece of this collection is a large, glass-topped cabinet, about the size of a coffin. And fit for purpose, since encased within it are the remains of a human body; a skeleton.

BLACKPINES theme

There is some limited literature in the way of interpretation. But the macabre details of the remains tell a story in themselves.

The skeleton is without a head. That is to say, its head lies at its feet. The body is turned

20

downwards, away from the observer, with the skull staring upwards; apparently to replicate the way in which it was buried and, subsequently, discovered.

Perhaps the most unnerving detail is this: protruding from the mouth of the skull is a large stone. From the cracked and broken teeth, it's plain enough to see that the stone was wedged in with some considerable force.

MUSIC stops

The Storyteller sits.

2.

STORYTELLER: I tell you about this grisly spectacle because it is pertinent to the tale I am going to share.

The following passages are taken, primarily, from the logbook of one Dr Abigail Hoffman. In the autumn of 1963, Dr Hoffman was summoned from the mainland, to the Isle of Shorehollow, by her brother.

At the time of writing, the Reverend Michael Hoffman had recently taken residence as the new priest of Blackpines.

21

3.

HOFFMAN: My dearest Abigail. Please, come at once.

I write to you in the gravest of health. Having you by my side would be a tremendous comfort.

Pious, obedient fool that I am, I thought the Lord would protect me, always.

I saw it, Abigail. The terrible, dark thing of which they warned me. I saw it and it left its mark upon me.

Do hurry.

Humbly and forever your brother,

Michael

4.

(Note: A crucial visual detail is that Abigail is missing a finger. This can be achieved by tucking the left ring-finger into a fingerless glove, or bending the finger to the palm whenever necessary.)

From this point, The Storyteller recounts the tale from Abigail's point of view.

ABIGAIL: 4th September '63

***THE RECTORY** theme*

I arrived at the old rectory at six o'clock and was admitted by a small-statured man who introduced himself as Mr Palfreman. He acts as both housekeeper and verger to Michael.

He seemed friendly, kind, hospitable. Facts which only contributed to my shock when I discovered that Michael had been locked in his room by the verger since falling ill.

Mr Palfreman leaves a tray of food and fluids twice a day, but has not seen Michael in the flesh for almost a week.

He is fearful of infection, I suppose. Though he does seem a nervy sort of a fellow in general.

Abigail moves to MICHAEL'S ROOM.

Throughout our initial conversation, Mr Palfreman seemed rather preoccupied with my left hand. It took me a moment to realise he was staring at my *finger* with some alarm.

Abigail reveals the missing finger.

MUSIC stops

'Oh, it's alright,' I told him. 'Lost it to frostbite on the Shetlands some years back. Fear not! I'm perfectly able to practise medicine without it!'

This did not seem to remedy his intrigue nor soothe his agitation.

8pm: same day

I have examined Michael. The prognosis is not good.

THE RECTORY *theme*

His lucidity is fleeting. But he does, episodically, appear to know who I am. Upon seeing me for the first time, he began to weep effusively.

Takes out examination notes

The flesh around his eye sockets is raw and the eyes themselves are shockingly bloodshot.

His breathing is addled and constricted.

There are welts on his flesh and - so far as I can make out from his fingernails - some self-inflicted scratches. I have bound his hands to prevent this from worsening.

He is frequently hysterical; repeatedly speaking of some *thing* which enters his room at night and - to use Michael's expression - *feeds* on him. He has feverishly asked me to check him for bite marks several times.

It is clear to me that the respiratory fever from which my brother is suffering has lead to a range of other symptoms; one of which appears to be (*writes*) advanced psychosis.

MUSIC stops

*

24

I shall not stay at the public house as Mr Palfreman has suggested. I shall make up a room here, at the rectory.

5.

The RECTORY

ABIGAIL: 5th September

Today I managed a brief, disjointed conversation with Mr Palfreman.

He described to me the evening on which Michael became ill.

BLACKPINES *theme*

PALFREMAN: He fell through the door, miss. Weak as a kitten. Rambling about something that'd happened in the woods. I warned him. We don't go in there.

It was on account of the rain, you see. Cutting through the woods from the town is much quicker. But we walk around, miss. Always.

The Reverend kept on about some *thing* that had attacked him. Bit him, he said. He was weeping. Weeping and praying.

I told him to sit and I'd fix him a drink. Just sit. Sit a while -

(As Michael) slowly lowers himself onto the chair.

As soon as he makes contact, he leaps up, screams in pain, grabbing his leg. This should be sudden and shocking.

MUSIC stops suddenly

PALFREMAN: The way he leapt up from that chair! Said that something had burned his leg. I half expected to see an ember from the fire but… no.

I helped him to his bedroom. And there he's been since.

ABIGAIL: Mr Palfreman seemed to be on the verge of telling me something else, but then hesitated. I implored him to go on.

BLACKPINES theme

PALFREMAN: Well… it's just that… I had a mind to investigate what the Reverend fancied had burned him when he sat in his chair.

There was only one thing there. Only one thing it could have been.

Finds/produces a crucifix. This can be hidden somewhere on the chair.

His cross. His crucifix.

He holds the crucifix aloft, almost brandishing it as a defensive weapon.

It was then that I locked him in his room.

MUSIC stops

ABIGAIL: Mr Palfreman would tell me no more.

*

Michael's condition is worsening. I do not believe he will survive the week.

6.

MICHAEL'S ROOM

ABIGAIL: 6th September

Sitting by Michael's bedside for most of today. Administering sedatives is the limit of my powers, I fear.

Picks up book.

DEAD THING *theme*

I have been passing the time by reading about the history of the isle. It appears always to have been a place rife with superstition (indeed a chapter in one volume refers to the belief that missing fingers are a mark of The Devil - perhaps this explains the verger's odd reaction!)

I am beginning to understand Mr Palfreman's circumspect references to the Blackpines forest, too. Though I do not share the superstitious beliefs which plainly still resonate in this community, the similarities to my brother's circumstances documented in this volume are, I must admit, quite chilling.

HISTORIAN:

*NB: Words in **bold** indicate lines that Abigail reads out, also.*

In the winter of 1686, a young woodsman by the name of Gregory Muller returned from Blackpines forest in a state of acute agitation.

He talked of some **'dead thing'** that he claimed had stalked and bitten him in the woods.

Muller retired to bed, whereupon he became suddenly and gravely ill.

His symptoms were as follows: **irritated and bloodshot eyes, contusions and laceration-like marks** across the body, **painful and strained breathing.**

ABIGAIL: Identical to Michael!

HISTORIAN: He died in considerable agony and continued raving about the **dead thing** he claimed had attacked him until the last. He maintained that the thing kept returning at night **to feed on him.**

ABIGAIL: It's uncanny!

HISTORIAN: Muller claimed that the spectre resembled his father - who had died not six weeks previously.

Muller's body was buried in the cemetery at **the centre of Blackpines forest.**

A week later, his wife and six children all came down **with the same symptoms**. And similar macabre visions were reported by all.

ABIGAIL: Perhaps some manner of mass hysteria.

HISTORIAN: The illness became an epidemic. All affected died. All were buried in Blackpines forest. All claimed to have seen the risen dead in their homes and dwellings.

MUSIC stops

ABIGAIL: The risen dead?

HISTORIAN: Being a superstitious age, the townsfolk sought solutions in ungodly places...

ABIGAIL: (*Continues to read*) Being a superstitious age, the townsfolk sought solutions in ungodly places. A band of men ventured into Blackpines forest. Each had a rudimentary mask attached to his face to insulate him from the stench of death. Each, too, wore a crucifix.

They dug up the newly-buried corpses and made a horrendous discovery. The mouths of the bodies were filled with blood...

BLACKPINES theme

This was proof enough that the dead were indeed rising and feeding on the living.

A most barbaric burial ritual was devised and practised:

They decapitated the corpses; turning the bodies downwards to face hell; placing their severed heads at their feet, turned upwards towards heaven.

And, finally, the men thrust large rocks between the jaws of the dead. To stop them from feeding.

Soon, the forest became off-limits to all townsfolk. A place no-one in their right mind should go - lest some dark thing might follow them home.

After taking dozens of lives, the strange plague began to subside and the townsfolk attributed this 'miracle' to the unholy measures they had taken.

MUSIC stops

Puts book down.

It's the forest. The forest is the key.

7.

BLACKPINES VILLAGE.

ABIGAIL: 7th September

Mr Palfreman continues to avoid every question I have about Blackpines' history.

I had begun to wonder if the rest of the townsfolk would be similarly tight-lipped.

So, on the pretence of collecting medicine, I asked Mr Palfreman to mind Michael while I took a trip into the town. He would not let me leave without my giving him the key to my brother's room.

It is very plain to me now that the village does not welcome outsiders. Perhaps it was my inquisitive nature which earned me such a taciturn reception. Shrugs and grunts from almost everybody.

After a few hours with no success, I decided to try a different approach: provocation.

When in the grain store I spoke to an old woman; the proprietor. I mentioned that the gathering rain clouds were tempting me to take the shortcut through the woods on my return to the rectory.

She insisted she drive me home immediately; closing her shop to do so. I was unable to argue and was forcefully obliged into her vehicle. She would not speak to me for the duration of the journey.

As I climbed out of her van, the woman called after me:

'He should have listened to us.'

8.

MICHAEL'S ROOM

Throughout, Abigail holds onto Michael's crucifix.

MICHAEL'S DEATH theme

ABIGAIL: 8th September, 11pm.

We lost Michael tonight.

His last few hours were acutely traumatic. His hallucinations peaked in a most distressing fashion. He became convinced - utterly convinced - that there was an evil of some sort in the house with us. May he rest in peace, now.

I have laid him out, washed him, dressed him and covered him.

She studies the crucifix.

I am engaged in a rotten row with Mr Palfreman. He wishes to take responsibility for Michael's burial. Absolutely out of the question.

The boat to the mainland is in two days. There must be somebody on this wretched island who is willing to assist me with transportation of the body. I am sure of it.

Poor, poor Michael.

Pause

I was somewhat unnerved by something Palfreman said as he left:

'The Reverend will have to be dealt with. One way or another.'

I insisted he hand over any keys he had for the rectory.

MUSIC stops

9.

ABIGAIL: I have decided to go into the woods.

I know that this would have upset Michael. But I suspect the forest holds crucial information about the source of his illness. This decision can only be of benefit to the people of the isle.

Even in the face of such stubbornness and superstition, I feel the burden of my Hippocratic oath.

Picks up a medical bag.

10.

THE FOREST theme

Abigail ventures into the woods as the music plays. After a short while, she returns and moves downstage.

MUSIC stops

ABIGAIL: (*Traumatised*) I must get this down whilst it is fresh in my mind.

What a Godless place that forest is! The way those skeletal trees climb into the sky, like the hands of the damned reaching, hopelessly, from hell...

Pause

The day was misty and traversing the forest made for slow progress. I followed an overgrown path and, after a short while, came upon an area where the denseness of the trees thinned a little.

I could see large stones jutting from the ground and knew at once I had reached the old cemetery. I thought of those poor souls beneath the sod; buried in that heinous way.

Opens case

Much of the ground, many of the rocks and tree trunks were covered in a thick, black-ish matter. Perhaps algae of some kind. Its proliferation intrigued me.

Takes out a glass sample jar containing a strange, black substance. Studies and inspects it.

I decided to collect a sample and capture some photographs of the area for observation, later. Carefully, I scraped a little of the substance into one of my sample jars. Then, I took up my camera.

*MUSIC - **sparse, low, bell-like notes***

At first I thought it was a smudge on the lens; or, simply the way the light was dispersing through the mist... but another look scotched those thoughts in an instant.

Perhaps a dozen figures were standing dumbly by a row of listing graves. They were uncannily still and all focused on a single spot.

How could I have missed them before? But I had no time to dwell on this maddening thought for, a moment later, I saw the focus of their attention.

Some manner of vaguely human thing stood upright in front of the fearful crowd. It was a great deal taller than any person I have ever seen.

At first, it appeared to me to be wrapped in some dark garment. But I was wrong. It was without clothes entirely and a dense hair - no, not hair - *fur* - covered its body.

Its face was not that of a man - more hircine, goat-like, in appearance - but its expressions were revoltingly, unmistakably human. Its fingers were webbed; grey flesh stretched between each digit; a thin flap of skin connected its arms to its body. It was

35

gesturing to the deathly figures as a shepherd might to his flock.

MUSIC stops

(*Whispered*) I tried to rise, undetected; to run! But the evil thing moved as if it had caught a foreign scent on the air...

MUSIC - bursts of bow

It looked directly at me.

That remarkable expression! What burned in its eyes was an intelligent fury, an outrage at having been discovered.

It snorted and spat and raised its webbed arms.

As one, the other figures turned towards me. They had the corrupted faces of dead men.

They began to advance.

MUSIC - frantic bowing

Pushes through the forest, impeded.

I pushed my way through the trees as fast as I could; the tangle of undergrowth catching at my feet. I ran and I ran, stumbling often, and soon I began to hear their voices behind me: hollow, dry, desiccated sounds.

And then I felt them scratching at my back. Pulling at my hair. A cold hand closed around my neck. Another reached around to my face. I felt its fingers fumbling at my eyes, my nose, my mouth…

MUSIC stops

And then the very ground beneath me was gone.

MUSICAL FLOURISH

Abigail falls to her knees.

If it had not been for the forest's steep bank, I would not have escaped them. I tumbled painfully to the bottom of the hill.

When I came to and looked up the dark bank, I saw those terrible, dead things retreating backwards into the trees.

*

I barely remember the journey back to Michael's house. But when I arrived there, the front door stood open.

They had taken his body.

ABIGAIL'S theme

11.

THE RECTORY

ABIGAIL: (*Manic, hysterical*) I'm going to hide my logbook beneath the floorboards.

The welts have begun to surface on my skin. My eyes are unbearably sore. Breathing is an extreme difficulty. Each cough is sticky and painful. And I too am beginning to see the dark things that creep in the shadows.

For two nights the townsfolk have been coming.

I have seen them from the window. They took Michael. They want to take me, too.

They are waiting for me to die. And I know what they would do with me.

*

They are here again now but the door is strong, the locks secure. The windows are too high to break through.

They come at night and so I only need wait for the morning. If I can just get to the shore. To the boat.

Abigail discovers the sample jar in a pocket, looks at it. A revelation comes.

The substance I collected from the forest…

MUSIC stops

12.

THE RECTORY reprise

STORYTELLER: Dr Hoffman's account ends abruptly here.

There are, however, two further points of interest in the case:

Firstly, two years ago, a team of pedologists visited the Isle of Shorehollow on a research expedition to study the soils of the areas surrounding Blackpines Forest.

The team inadvertently discovered a mutated culture of s*tachybotrys chartarum*: the scientific name for black mould.

Research is in its early stages. However, there is an indication that the culture can, in rare cases, provoke symptoms similar to those described in Dr Hoffman's account: welts on the skin, respiratory trauma, ocular irritation, blood in the mouth post-mortem and, in cases that are rarer still, psychosis.

Secondly: the research team made another, more disturbing find.

When surveying the land around the old rectory, a lead-lined coffin was discovered in a shallow grave. In it, human remains, which had been desecrated in the same way that has been described here.

That same skeleton is now exhibited in a coffin-sized glass case, in a dingy back room of the Blackpines Library. And if you were ever to visit the Isle of Shorehollow and find yourself face-to-face with that macabre spectacle, you might notice a small detail that could easily go undetected by most:

ABIGAIL'S theme

If you look closely at the skeleton you'll see that the ring finger of the left hand is missing.

MUSIC stops

*

STORYTELLER: Wherever our journey takes us, the world over, the darkest and most horrifying aspects of life are often to be found in the unwise actions of the fearful.

ACT 2

DEAD AIR

STORYTELLER: Our next tale brings us a little closer to home.

The stories in the book can take many different forms. Tales can arise from the most unlikely of places.

The following is taken from a transcript of a radio broadcast, on a now defunct local station, in the early 1990s.

We join so-called spirit medium Alice Hope, as she and her producer work what is commonly referred to as the graveyard shift... late-night talk radio.

(*NB: The following can be staged as a duologue or Alice's parts can be pre-recorded. The Storyteller takes on the persona of David.*)

FX: RADIO STATIC

FX: HELLISH SOUNDS MERGE INTO...

FX: RADIO JINGLE/STING/INTRO

ALICE: You're listening to VITAL FM. It's late night spirit talk with me, Alice Hope. I'm here as ever with Producer Paul. Later on I'm going to be doing a reading for one lucky listener. But now, and for the next hour, we are inviting *you* to call in with your *true ghost stories*.

Yes, we've just heard from Julie in Bramwell. My love to her. *Was* it the ghost of her dog Belle? Or just the ancient pipes of the house howling in the night? Call me on 0422 13 13 and let me know what you think.

Next up we have David on the phones. Now David has a story about his *grandmother*, I believe. Good evening David...

FX: SUDDEN STATIC - SCREAM - BUZZ

ALICE: Oh, apologies there. *A ghost in the machine*, Paul? (*Laughs*) What was that? He doesn't know. Bless him. Ah, lovely Paul. I think we have him now - David. Good evening... David?

DAVID: (*Pause*) Hello?

ALICE: Welcome to the show, David.

DAVID: (*Pause*) Thank you.

ALICE: You've got a ghost story to tell us...

DAVID: Well... I mean, I don't know that I'd call it a 'ghost story'.

ALICE: Ooh, you're not one of the sceptic brigade, are you David? (*Laughs*)

DAVID: Oh, no... I mean... it's just I don't... I haven't got an explanation for this.

ALICE: Don't you worry, my love. Leave the explanations to me. It's about your grandmother, is that right?

DAVID: Yes.

ALICE: And she's no longer with us?

DAVID: Yes. I mean, no. No, she's not.

ALICE: I'm sorry to hear that David but you're happy to tell us the story?

DAVID: (*Pause. Breathing*)

ALICE: David?

DAVID: (*Jumps*) Sorry! I don't normally call these things. I'm a bit nervous. Sorry.

ALICE: No need to be sorry my love. You're in safe hands. You go on...

DEAD AIR theme

DAVID: Well, it's as you say. It's about my grandmother. She used to live in this enormous house. With this big, overgrown garden. Tall dead grass. I remember it really clearly.

ALICE: That's lovely, David. You're painting the picture for us...

DAVID: (*Smiles, a little more relaxed*) Oh! Well, erm... She was... mean, I suppose you'd say. She was horrible, really. Unpleasant. Unkind. But also… well, *tight.* A miser. Worth a fortune but never seemed to spend anything. On herself or anyone else. If something broke in the house, it stayed broken, you know what I mean?

ALICE: I think we all know people like that, David!

DAVID: (*Laughs, unsure*) Well anyway. She, uh, she became quite frail. Wasn't able to do a lot for herself. She could afford to pay for help - more than afford. Only she wouldn't.

Instead, she insisted on daily visits from my mum and my auntie. (*Remembering fondly*) Auntie Sheila. They'd run her errands. Do all the housework in that huge house. All the washing. Change all the beds - even though she was the only one who lived there. And she mostly slept in her chair.

There was no affection. No love. It was like a business transaction. She was always threatening to cut them off. You know, financially? Always threatening to change her will.

ALICE: Oh, she sounds a bugger.

DAVID: That's one way of putting it.

DEAD AIR theme develops

She lived out of one room in that huge house.

The room, I remember, was really long and mostly empty. The floorboards were damp; rotting.

The walls were covered in mildew and the paper was peeling. It stank in there.

When we visited, my mum would take big bunches of lavender from our garden to put in vases along the edge of the room. She said it was to cheer my grandmother up but I knew it was to cover the smell.

It made it worse, if anything. Now, whenever I smell lavender, all I can think about is her. And that horrible room.

My grandmother would sit at the end of the room, staring out of these floor-to-ceiling... erm, are they *bay* windows, those ones? You know the sort I mean?

ALICE: I do, love. You get them in Victorian houses, don't you?

DAVID: Yeah, you do, yeah! (*Pause*) So she'd sit staring out of these bay windows. She'd pull this curtain around behind her. But the curtain was mouldy. It was covered in these green stains.

I remember going into that room, every time, and seeing that curtain, with her shadow behind it.

I can see it now. If I close my eyes, I can see it.

MUSIC stops

ALICE: These memories have a tendency to linger, don't they, my love? Particularly with people who have passed over.

DAVID: (*Nods*)... She hated me.

ALICE: Oh, now, I'm sure that's not true...

DAVID: (*Spits*) It is true.

MUSIC stops

Sorry. It is true. But she insisted on me being there on my mum's visits.

She'd stare at me; her lip curled in disgust. I think... I think she enjoyed the fact that I was scared of her.

She'd criticise everything I did.

GRANDMOTHER notes - high and piercing

'Look at you. A slob. Still failing in school? Still the dunce of the class?' - I wasn't very good at school but I tried - 'Stand up straight and pronounce your words properly when you speak to me. Where are your manners? Disgusting, *vile* boy.'

MUSIC stops

ALICE: Oh, it sounds awful. Didn't your mum ever say anything?

DAVID: She looked upset when my grandmother started on at me. But, to tell you the truth, I think she was scared that if she stood up to her or said anything she'd be cut out of the will. I know it sounds like a pathetic reason when you say it out loud.

But they were only words, weren't they? Words can't really hurt you, can they? Not really.

ALICE: I don't know that I'd agree with that, David. I think your mum should have told her where to go. Dragging you along like that. Honestly…

DAVID: (*Snaps*) She did her best.

The visits were one thing. But the *phone calls*. She'd call almost every evening. Demand to speak to me after she was done with my mum.

At least when we visited her, I could wander off; perhaps to another room while she was whinging on at my mum.

GRANDMOTHER notes - high and piercing

But on the phone… she was there. Inside my head. With no witnesses.

47

It sounds daft but I actually developed a phobia of telephones as a kid because of it. I still have it a little bit.

Pause.

This is harder than I thought it would be.

ALICE: We appreciate you calling, my love. You're very brave.

DAVID: Whenever I hear a phone ring, still...

She said some dreadful things to me on those calls. Things you wouldn't believe. She was just... evil. I remember thinking she was evil. Ruined my confidence.

Sorry, I'm getting off the track...

Pause.

The night my grandmother died...

Pause.

Sorry. Actually, I'm not sure I can do this.

ALICE: (*Somewhat irritated*) It's alright my love. We're here. You take your time.

DEAD AIR theme, diminished

DAVID: (*Deep breath*) The night my grandmother died - I would have been twelve I think - something happened.

Something I can't explain.

48

I had this dream.

I was standing in that long, rotten room. Looking at that disgusting curtain.

And then, suddenly, I was moving towards it. I was sort of... floating is the only way I can describe it. I couldn't stop myself.

My shoes were scraping on the wooden floor; pulling up chunks of wet wood.

I knew, before I got to that curtain, what I'd find. I just knew.

I could see her shadow. Sitting in that chair.

And then I was at the curtain.

My hand moved up to it and - oh, God, I didn't want to - but I pulled it back.

MUSIC stops

It was my grandmother's corpse.

GRANDMOTHER sting - high and piercing

But she was... her *flesh* was... (*breaks*)

DEAD AIR theme returns

She was wrapped in a sheet. But it was filthy. As if she'd been buried in the ground, without a coffin, and dug up again to be put in that chair.

And her mouth moved. Her dead mouth.

A voice came from somewhere deep inside her.

MUSIC stops

And she said, 'Look at what you've done. I know. I know what you did.'

I woke up with those words ringing in my ears.

'I know what you did.'

ALICE: David this is... really quite disturbing.

DAVID: I know. Please let me finish... I've called for your help, you see. I think you can *help*, Alice...

ALICE: I'm not sure what you think I can do... I can give you a number for...

DAVID: No! Please, just listen.

When I woke up... I thought that I could smell lavender. In my room.

Then the phone began to ring, downstairs.

I heard my mum get up to answer it.

She spoke quietly at first and then... she screamed for my dad:

'OH MY GOD, MARCUS!'

I jumped out of bed, I wanted to find out what was wrong.

And I knew, before I'd even seen it, that there was something in the room with me.

Sitting in the corner.

Wrapped in a filthy sheet.

THING IN THE CORNER *theme*

I tried to run for the door but the thing jerked forwards, reached out with its dead hands and grabbed me. I could feel its bones through the sheet. I tried to get free but I couldn't. I could hear her voice again. 'I KNOW WHAT YOU DID!'

I screamed. I screamed for my mum and my dad.

And then everything went black.

MUSIC *stops*

Blackout.

*

The next thing I remember: I was lying on the settee. My dad said he'd found me in my room. Passed out. He didn't mention... anything else.

I must have been dreaming, I told myself. Must have still been dreaming.

My mum was at the hospital.

My grandmother had died in the night. My Auntie Sheila had found her early that morning.

Later, I overheard my parents talking.

GRANDMOTHER *notes - high and piercing*

My mum said that my grandmother had died with the telephone in her hand. She was trying to call for help. My mum said that if someone'd got to her sooner she wouldn't have died.

I felt so... awful. So guilty...

ALICE: It sounds to me like you're blaming yourself there. And let me tell you...

DAVID: But it was my fault.

ALICE: David, when we have bad feelings towards people and then they pass away...

DAVID: NO, *LISTEN.*

THE CUT *theme*

On our last visit to my grandmother, she was on at me as usual. Worse than ever. Saying I was a drain on my parents. Calling me - what was it? - a vile, ill-mannered boy.

Again, my mum said nothing.

I'd had enough. I stormed out of the room. And my grandmother laughed at me! Called me a *wimp*! A big baby.

I thought: I'll show her.

I wanted to do some damage. I wanted to hurt her. But I knew she didn't care about anything.

And then it came to me. What I'd do.

I took out my penknife. I traced the wire along the wall to the corner where it plugged in.

And I cut it.

I cut her phone line.

It was just a silly thing, really. I didn't think anything would happen. I'd just had enough of her.

She tried to call for help and she couldn't.

She died because of me.

MUSIC stops

ALICE: Oh, my love. Look, there are many times when we...

DAVID: And now... every year...

She comes back.

ALICE: I'm sorry, David? I don't follow.

DAVID: THIS IS WHY I CALLED YOU! I wanted your help. I don't know how to stop it. I want to stop it.

LOW drone

Every year. On the same day. The day she died. First it's the smell of lavender. Then the phone starts ringing. That voice, saying those same words... and then she's there... in the room... wrapped in that filthy shroud... trying to reach for me with those dead hands... and I can't bear it any more... I can't bear it... I can't...

FX: DEAFENING CRACKLE ON LINE

ALICE: Now, calm down, David... Paul, can we...?

FX: CRACKLE ON LINE - TRACE OF A VOICE

DAVID: I thought... this year... if I could keep the line busy... I could stop her breaking through.

I'm so sorry, Alice.

'I know what you did!' That's what she says.

I'm so sorry!

What time is it? Can't you hear her? Can you hear her? LISTEN!

FX: SHOCKING STATIC

ALICE: David? Are you there, my love? We've lost him. Apologies. We'll make sure our aftercare team look after David.

Well, I feel like we all need a breather after David's story...

FX: LOUD PHONE TONE

Oh (*nervous laugh*) sorry about this. Paul, are we... on air?

(*Panicked tone*) Paul...? Paul are we... on air? Paul?

Sudden blackout

Oh... the lights have just gone off.

Paul... someone's just come in... Paul, who's that? *There!*

FX: CRACKLE. DREADFUL, MALEVOLENT VOICE: 'I KNOW WHAT YOU DID!'

In the corner! Who is it? *Who is it?* Oh my GOD...

FX: RADIO STATIC, THE TERRIBLE VOICE RISES, WHITE NOISE, CRESCENDO... A HORRIFYING, BLOOD-CURDLING SCREAM FROM THE DARKNESS.

Lights come up to reveal an empty stage.

INTERVAL

ACT 3

A HORROR IN PORCELAIN

1.

The Musician enters.

MUSIC - frantic stabs

The Storyteller enters.

MUSIC stops

STORYTELLER: You might suppose us to be the book's keepers. But you would be wrong. It does not belong to us. We belong to it.

After each gathering we draw, I pray to see empty pages; a sign that the book is finished with us. A sign that we have been released from our sentences; set free. But...

Goes to speak. Picks up and downs whisky instead.

So we come to our final tale of the evening.

It requires very little in the way of introduction from me.

But I will say this: All of the stories in this book are filled with the stuff of nightmares. But no tale has ever chilled me the way this one does.

MUSIC - A HORROR IN PORCELAIN theme

2.

From this point, The Storyteller recounts the tale from Williams's point of view.

WILLIAMS: Since I do not intend for these papers to see the light of day in my lifetime, I feel rather at liberty to tell the truth. And I trust that my account will be accepted as such. For this is true. Every word of it.

Of a recent duty assigned to me, I have a rather evil story to share. I shall, for the sake of discretion, refer to my employer as Delaney.

He is neither a wise nor a moral man. But he is, lately, a haunted one.

The tale begins, rather absurdly, with a child's plaything. An antique doll, dating from the early 1700s.

This was not the first collectible toy that I had been charged with obtaining by Mr. Delaney, but it was certainly the most notable and the most expensive. Indeed, according to some experts on the topic, and for reasons I shall come to, the doll is supposed to be priceless.

The simplest way to explain Delaney's bizarre hobby is by characterising him not so much as a collector, but as a jailer.

DELANEY theme

> Sequestered away in many rooms of his considerable house are hundreds of rare dolls, toys and playthings, which he has acquired over the years. Their accumulated value I would estimate to be in the several millions of pounds.

> I've often reflected upon the nature of a man who takes pleasure in seeing such items locked up and hidden away where they can never be played with nor appreciated as they were intended to be.

> 'I am assembling a treasure trove,' Delaney once said to me.

> 'A legacy.'

MUSIC stops

> He has no children; nor nieces or nephews. He is, indeed, the end of the Delaney line.

DELANEY theme once

3.

DOROTHY'S CAR

WILLIAMS: And so, on a gloomy Friday in December of last year, I began the long, dull journey to the Grayhampton Toy Museum.

Mr Delaney's long-suffering chauffeur - Dorothy - had kindly offered to give me a lift to the station.

Ah, Dorothy. She is as indiscreet as she is acerbically witty. I like her a great deal.

Driving

'What is it this time?' she asked as we drove along.

'A doll,' I responded.

'He's not right, that one. Fancy a grown man hiding dolls away in his house. It's his money lets him do it. If I started taking toys as prisoners, they'd send the white van for me.'

When I told Dorothy how much Delaney had paid for the new item - which was in six figures - she all but crashed the car.

'*Ow much*? Shall I tell you what he pays me? I'm about to be outranked by a bloody dolly! What's so special about it?'

PALE LORD *motif*

4.

WILLIAMS: I suspect you may indeed be wondering what was so special about this particular doll. Well, allow me to explain.

It wasn't the doll's considerable age that made it such a coveted treasure. Nor the toymaker or particular model.

No. This doll was so valued because of the identity of its original owner.

PALE LORD motif

If you have any interest in English folklore - particularly of the late-Georgian period - you may be familiar with the stories relating to Sir Nicodemus Barlow; often referred to as The Pale Lord.

PALE LORD motif

An incessant manchild; a cruel, malicious recluse. Despite his education, his privilege and his intelligence, the notorious Pale Lord chose to conduct himself in a most petulant, peevish and pugnacious manner. He was much-feared and little understood.

PALE LORD motif

Barlow's boyhood collection of toys is well-documented. So, too, is the condition in which he left them. The Pale Lord was known to disfigure and mutilate his dolls and playthings in most disturbing ways.

The particular doll I was on this quest for, for instance, had had its eyes removed by Barlow.

These eerie mutilations are the distinguishing features of what have come to be known collectively as 'The Children of Barlow'.

PALE LORD theme

The Pale Lord's destructive early behaviour was a mild foreshadowing of his adult crimes, however. As he grew into a man, Barlow turned his violent hand to many a peasant who irked him or servant who tried to deny him something that he wanted.

He became less and less satisfied with torturing things without feelings, and turned his malicious attentions to the living.

Or, so the stories will have it.

MUSIC stops

*

DOROTHY'S CAR

I told Dorothy none of this (she's not fond of things that '*give her the willies*') and instead invented something about the doll having a unique manufacturing defect.

'Ey, why don't you pinch it and sell it and we can run away together!' Dorothy said as she lifted my bag from the boot.

'Now, don't be cruel,' I said. 'You're happily married. Don't torture me with empty promises!'

She broke into glorious laughter and we said our goodbyes.

5.

TOY MUSEUM

GRAYHAMPTON *theme*

WILLIAMS: The train journey was without incident and, despite the plodding speed of the little engine, I arrived good and early at the Grayhampton Toy Museum.

I was greeted and shown into the main gallery by a pleasant, rather shy young man.

'Mr Winstanley will be along shortly,' said the lad and ambled off into another part of the museum.

The walls of the main gallery were lined with shelves and cabinets. The gaze of many a goblin, stuffed animal and Jack-in-the-box was upon me and I noted that, in the right circumstances, these toys might be quite unnerving.

As I took in the motley collection, I began to wonder just how I would be received by Mr Winstanley, the museum's chief curator. The road to this transaction had not been a smooth one.

MUSIC stops

*

Delaney had bullied, cajoled and harangued his way to possession of the doll in his typically crooked fashion.

Mr Winstanley was loath to give up the Barlow doll. Indeed, he protested over some thirteen letters and in excess of twenty telephone calls. He asserted - quite correctly in my view - that the appropriate place for such a unique item was, indeed, a museum where it could be properly restored and preserved.

The culmination of the whole affair was a bitter telegram from Delaney to his cronies at Brindleshire Council - the main benefactors of the toy museum. This provoked a reluctant but speedy change of heart in Mr Winstanley.

*

GRAYHAMPTON theme

Even after I had looked twice around the collection in the main gallery, Mr Winstanley had not appeared and so I decided upon a short, unaccompanied perusal of the rest of the place.

I hadn't wandered very far before finding myself in a room with rather dim lighting. The shelves and cabinets in this room were mostly bare - evidently a new collection was due to be installed.

However, in one corner there was a single, tall case. It was full of dolls and toys with a unifying quality: each had had a part of its body removed.

Some had had an arm torn from them; others, a leg ripped off. Some appeared to have had their hair singed to the scalp and one particular horror had had its nose tweezed clean away.

I read the information at the side of the case:

EXPERT: The Children of Barlow: A collection of dolls which have, over the years, been attributed to the former possession of the fabled Sir Nicodemus Barlow, otherwise known as The Pale Lord. However, closer inspection of each of these items has revealed them to be...

WILLIAMS: 'Fakes!' This was yelled by a man now standing just over my shoulder.

As Winstanley: stoops to pick up an old wooden box.

'Each and every one a fake. People will go to all kinds of lengths if they think they can make a bob or two...'

He approached me and extended his hand.

'Edward Winstanley. Yes, we only have one true Child of Barlow in our collection. Well, we did have... until your employer... enquired after it. She is perhaps the only one left in England.'

'Still. Unnerving, aren't they?' I said, trying to shift the attention away from the awkward transaction at hand.

'Perhaps. To the fanciful. Not a patch on the real thing. There are some who claim that The Pale Lord possesses each doll he disfigured. That one can see him staring back from behind their eyes.'

'Is that so?' I said, reaching for the box, impatiently.

'I mean, one can understand there being some spooky tales attached to the things. You'll be aware of how The Pale Lord met his end, I suppose?'

I sighed and shook my head. I was eager to make the return journey.

'A fire. His whole manor burned to the ground. Barlow had been locked in his room by his staff and left to die. If you believe the legend - which I myself do not - The Pale Lord's body was nowhere to be found afterwards. But his dolls and toys... had all

65

survived. Then the looters came. That's why the real Children of Barlow have been so hard to track over the years.'

He handed me the box. Something clunked, dully, inside.

FX DULL CLUNK

And all of a sudden... there's no other way to express this... I dreaded the contents.

PALE LORD motif

'Well, thank you Mr Winstanley. I won't keep you any longer.'

'You'll know, of course,' he went on, 'about the stories surrounding this particular doll?'

'Mm? Stories? What? What stories? No, I haven't heard any stories...'

'Oh... well. It's not for me to say.'

'Not for you to say? Why the devil did you bring it up, then? (*To self*) Bloody fool. (*To Winstanley*) In any case, I really must be going. Mr Delaney is expecting me...'

'One piece of advice before you go? When I acquired the doll I was instructed to keep everything exactly as I found it. I have done so. I suggest you and your employer do likewise.'

(*Laughs*) 'If you are offering advice on curation and preservation,' I said. 'I'm afraid you are wasting your breath. My employer is a fathead. A brute. This old thing will end up on a shelf and forgotten about in a very short while indeed. (*Turns to leave, turns back*) Oh, and if you repeat what I have just said about Mr Delaney, I shall simply deny it. Good day.'

'Mr Williams?'

I turned to see what the grinning imbecile wanted now.

His face was stony.

'Preservation is precisely the point. Keep the doll as it is.'

PALE LORD *motif*

I left at speed, Winstanley's insufferable wittering ringing in my ears like a persistent hornet.

Leaves the museum carrying the box.

6.

TRAIN CABIN

GRAYHAMPTON *theme, diminished*

Williams arrives in a train compartment, places the box down safely and sits.

WILLIAMS: On the train home I experienced some unfortunate delays.

After only an hour of travel, the whole locomotive stopped dead and gave no indication of progressing. It transpired that there was some gormless beast on the tracks that would not be moved.

I was alone in my compartment and had taken the opportunity to attend to some overdue correspondence. This completed, I was effectively twiddling my thumbs. I was about to go and beg a newspaper from a passenger in another compartment when the box caught my eye.

Picks up the box, inspects it.

Though old, it seemed to be in rather good condition. I noted the skilful carpentry, the delicacy of the little clasp on the front. Yes, it was a very good box indeed.

Drums fingers on box, whistles, looks around the carriage.

Well, I thought. What harm can come from merely looking at the thing?

I ran my thumb along the lid, contemplating this. An unbidden, not entirely pleasant thrill ran through me.

But, undeterred, I slowly and carefully opened the box.

MUSIC stops

Opens the box, keeping it facing away from the audience.

And there it was.

The pitiful, eyeless thing.

Exactly as it had appeared in Delaney's collectors' catalogue. The peach dress. The little bow. The deep, red hair. Identical...

But, no. No, not identical. Not entirely.

Because around the little thing's neck was a length of string; a sort of makeshift necklace with a piece of card affixed to it. On the card was some sort of rune or symbol: three interconnecting triangles.

VALKNUT flourish

'What an odd addition,' I thought.

I leant in to have a closer look... and Mr Winstanley's warning leapt into my brain with an upsetting ferocity.

WINSTANLEY: Keep the doll as it is.

Williams slams the box lid closed.

VALKNUT flourish

WILLIAMS: A second later, the train was moving again.

As I was safely stowing the box under my seat, I heard - so I supposed at the time - the guard shuffle into the carriage, no doubt to apologise for the delay.

I felt his shadow fall across me.

'About time too! I'm going to be very late indeed now. If this is what you call a train service…'

Williams gasps.

VALKNUT flourish

The carriage was empty. As it had been for the entire journey.

Stands up.

Outside, it had started to snow.

A HORROR IN PORCELAIN theme

7.

DELANEY'S LAND/HOUSE

WILLIAMS: Everything in sight was covered in a deep, white blanket when I finally reached Delaney's estate.

Dorothy had collected me from the station but could only take me as far as her cottage on the edge of Delaney's land.

'Let's have a peek at the doll!' Dorothy said.

I refused. It was a two mile walk, at least, to the house and I wanted to get there before it became too much darker.

When, at last, I got inside, the bottoms of my trouser legs, my shoes and my socks were sodden. I was frozen to the bone, and miserable.

There was a fire blazing in the hallway hearth - I was thankful for that, at least. And then I saw Delaney. He was pacing back and forth, making a tremendous show of checking his watch and sighing in a dramatic display of exasperation.

'Where the hell have you been?' he asked, as I brushed snow from my overcoat.

By way of answer, I opened the door and allowed a small blizzard to blow in.

'Yes, yes. Well. I was expecting you at four. It's gone six.'

'There were issues on the train,' I said 'And Dorothy couldn't get the car along the drive…'

'There's always an excuse, isn't there?'

Delaney's gaze fell upon the box in my arms. His eyes rounded and he lunged for it, throwing the lid open with animalistic relish.

'Ha-ha! Yes! Yes indeed. Look at her, Williams. Astonishing, isn't she?'

'She is,' I said, looking at the doll. 'Absolutely foul.'

'She's *beautiful*,' Delaney snapped. 'And do you know, I think she will take pride of place in my own bedroom this evening.'

This was somewhat surprising. As I have said, almost every item Delaney had ever procured ended up on a shelf, thick with dust, behind a locked door.

But, frankly, I was too exhausted to raise the issue.

'If it's alright, I think I'll make up a room for myself. The trains are no longer running and I'd like to rise early tomorrow to see if I can get home another way.'

He was not listening.

'What is this?'

He held up the wretched thing, his finger pulling at the string necklace around the doll's neck.

VALKNUT flourish

'Well…?' he boomed.

I squinted, keeping up a pretence that this was the first time I had properly laid eyes on the doll.

'I'm afraid I have no idea.'

Delaney scoffed and before I could stop him, he tore off the string, card and all, and threw it onto the fire.

VALKNUT *flourish*

He clumsily tipped the empty box onto the telephone table and wandered down the corridor; staring, adoringly, at his horrendous prize.

I noticed that a number of scraps of paper and cards had fallen out of the box.

One, it appeared, was a certificate of authenticity. The other bits and pieces were, on the whole, pages torn from books.

I could not read these without my eyeglasses and, these being somewhere in the depths of my bag, this was enough of a stimulus to send me, once and for all, to bed.

8.

WILLIAMS' BEDROOM

Williams sleeps. A sudden noise awakens him.

THE DOLL *theme*

WILLIAMS: (*Irritated, whispering*) I awoke in the small hours to a noise coming from the landing outside my room. A scuffling sound. That of light footsteps on carpet.

I realised to my extreme irritation that it must have been Delaney. Though what activity he was engaged in at... quarter to five in the morning, I could not imagine.

He was, so far as I could ascertain, scuttling past my door and then after a time, scuttling back in the other direction. This went on for the best part of *a quarter of an hour.*

After which time, I clicked on my sidelight and cleared my throat, loudly... (*Clears throat*)

MUSIC stops

His shadow stopped just outside my door. I could hear him breathing.

Well, I was damned if I was going to make conversation with the halfwit - *it was the middle of the night*! So I simply lay still and, eventually, he retreated in the direction of his own room, evidently dragging his feet petulantly behind him.

THE DOLL theme

I tried to get back to sleep but it was no good. I was wide awake.

74

> I cast my eyes around for something to read to help me drop off again. I spied the papers which had fallen out of the doll's box.

Puts glasses on, picks up papers.

> I reached over and started to read the first one I laid my hands upon.

> It was from a book called *The Occult in British Folklore* by Betty Beauchamp. The chapter was entitled: 'Barlow's Birth':

MUSIC stops

BEAUCHAMP: There are many myths and macabre tales surrounding the details of the birth of Sir Nicodemus Barlow. One account, taken from a collier who lived in the village at the foot of The Pale Lord's manor, goes as follows:

> 'There was talk of many black-cloaked men, all huddled around the lowing mother; incanting things under their breath. Anyone's guess, who, if any of them, was a surgeon.'

FX STRANGE BARNYARD NOISES. ANIMALS, A CRYING INFANT.

> 'The infant was brought into the world a stretched, pale thing. A sluggish beast who had luxuriated too long in the womb. The child was horrendously calm, fixing each man present with an intelligent stare.'

Williams begins to fall asleep.

*

Blinding white light.

Williams sits up suddenly, and gasps.

WILLIAMS: I must have nodded off... because the next thing I was aware of was a flood of white light in my room and the sight of Delaney standing over by the window, having just pulled back the drapes.

He was holding the doll; pointing it at me.

'I didn't have you down as a trickster, Williams!'

Both of them glared at me; one with terrible eyeless sockets; the other, eyes enormous with anger.

I croaked my first word of the day; 'Pardon?'

'Oh, he seeks pardon!' Delaney said this to the doll.

'Mr Delaney, I'm afraid I have no idea...'

'I found her on the hallway carpet this morning. Do you realise that if I - or God forbid, *you* - had trodden on her, it would most likely have caved in her face? And who, then, would have reimbursed me, Williams? The culprit, that's who.'

'I'm sorry, am I to take it that you are accusing me of moving your doll around during the night as a prank?'

'He admits it!' Again, to the doll.

'I certainly do not,' I said, sitting up. 'Perhaps you dropped it yourself when you were gallivanting up and down the landing at five this morning?'

In my tired state I had failed to keep my manners in check. Delaney's cheeks went purple. But his expression was one of bafflement, not bashfulness.

'Gallivanting up and down? Are you quite well? I didn't move from my room at all last night. Unless you're accusing me of somnambulism. Because you know how I feel about such nonsense...'

'Mr Delaney. I assure you - I swear to you - I did not move your doll.'

For a moment, I thought he believed me.

'No. You are discovered, sir. Take your chastisement like a man and do not even think of touching her again. Now get up. It's gone eight.'

It suddenly came to my attention why the room was quite so bright that morning. The night had brought another three feet of snow, at least. If I'd had any hopes of leaving for home that day, they were certainly dashed then.

9.

DELANEY'S HOUSE

***POWER CUT** theme*

WILLIAMS: I managed to avoid Delaney for the majority of that day. This was unexpected as I had supposed he might put me to work doing some menial task or other.

But, aside from our meals, which I cooked voluntarily and we ate together - I barely saw him.

A rather unwelcome surprise had greeted us that morning. The electricity supply - owing almost certainly to the weather conditions - was out. I spent much of the morning furnishing the hallways with candlesticks; lighting them as the sun began to set. I dug out a couple of battery-powered torches, too; the brightest of which I kept for myself.

Picks up and moves a battery-powered torch.

                    *

At supper, I brought a steaming urn of cony stew to the table, along with a few hunks of bread just south of stale. I rang the dinner gong but, even after ten minutes, Delaney did not appear. I knew that eating without him would earn me an earful; so I lay down my spoon and went in search of the great oaf.

Moves off in search. Goes to...

DELANEY'S LOUNGE

On a table sits the doll's box.

I found him in his lounge. The room stank of second-hand booze.

Delaney was staring into a dark corner of the room, which was barely touched by the flickering candle light.

There, on top of a lamp table, stood the wretched doll.

MUSIC stops

As he talks, Williams takes the doll out of the box, keeping the doll's back to the audience. It is horrendous, distressed, scary-looking, even from behind. Its dress is torn/burnt and its limbs look mangled.

Delaney's fondness for the thing from that morning appeared to have vanished. There was a peculiar note of fright in his expression.

'Mr Delaney,' I said. 'Mr Delaney? Dinner. A nice stewed rabbit.'

He spoke in a low voice.

'What does she remind you of, Williams?' he said. 'At once alive and dead. Both at the same time. I can't put my finger on it.'

Evidently, he was drunk.

'She moved.'

As he said this he flicked his eyes to me for just a moment.

My expression gave me away.

'Wipe that insolent look off your face. *I saw her move.*'

'But… it's a doll, sir.' I was trying not to veer too close to condescension. 'It can't move.'

'I know what I saw! I have been keeping my eye on her for the last hour. She has moved three times.'

'Mr Delaney…'

'Look if you don't believe me! Perhaps you'll believe your own eyes!'

I looked at the doll carefully. Undoubtedly, there was something uncanny about those empty eye sockets. I admitted as much to Delaney.

'No, no, no. *Look…*'

Williams leans in close to the doll.

SUDDEN, PIERCING NOTE

'THERE!' (*as Delaney*)

'Mr Delaney… it's the candle light.'

'No! It moved! *She moves!*'

'Look!' I said.

I showed him how the naturally shifting air of the house played with the flames.

'It's the candles. The shadows. Nothing else.'

Delaney's countenance softened.

He seemed, abruptly, rather embarrassed at his raving. But there was relief there, too.

'Candles. Yes. What else would it be? Well, I think in any case perhaps she - that is, *the doll*, should remain down here for tonight. Then, tomorrow, we'll find a space in the safe room for her - *it*. Yes. Now. Did you say there was venison for dinner?'

'Rabbit, sir.'

'Oh, I can't abide rabbit. A ridiculous meat.'

*

Outside the snow had finally stopped falling. The weather forecast on the wireless seemed to indicate that a vast rainstorm was due in the next couple of days, which was expected

to wash away the worst of the drifts. For now,
though, the road to Delaney's house was still
blocked.

A HORROR IN PORCELAIN theme

Williams returns the doll to its box and carries it to...

10.

WILLIAMS' BEDROOM

WILLIAMS: That evening in my bedroom I was rather
agitated and I found myself unable to drop
off, once again.

I took a small sleeping draft and flicked
through the papers I'd retrieved from the
doll's box.

At the bottom of the pile was a notably small
scrap of paper; brown with age and curled at
the edges.

On it: a few lines of hand-scribbled text,
followed by a small sketch of a familiar
symbol. Three interconnecting triangles.

VALKNUT flourish

BEAUCHAMP: The Valknut. An enigmatic and widely
discussed symbol associated with Norse
mythology. Historically, it has been used as a
symbol for protection and its interlocking
triangles appear to represent life, death and
undeath. Some hold the belief that removing

	the symbol from a protected artefact can unleash a curse upon the guilty culprit.
WILLIAMS:	(*Scared and agitated*) Oh hang it! I have had it with this damned doll!

11.

PALE LORD theme

WILLIAMS:	That night, in a feverish dream, I heard Delaney's footsteps again. This time they were louder; more pronounced. And there was something else. A sort of… giggle. High and excitable. That… of a child. But then dipping to become a low, cruel laughter.

12.

FX: A TERRIBLE CRY

WILLIAMS:	Delaney's screams woke me.
	I leapt out of bed and ran to his room.
	Arming myself with a candlestick, I barged in without knocking.
	The man's eyes were on stalks.
	He was staring at the doll which was standing in its sickly manner on his dressing table.
	'I left her downstairs,' he said. 'I swear it!' My employer looked at me, searchingly, and fell backwards, in a faint, onto his bed.

PALE LORD theme

13.

KITCHEN

WILLIAMS: Delaney and I were in the kitchen. He was sipping hot, sweet tea. It had taken several hours to calm him.

'I must insist that you share my room this evening.'

He detected my protest before it had happened. The rain had started, the snow was clearing and I had rather hoped to make a break for home.

'I shall pay you. Double... *triple* your day rate. Just for this evening. Williams... please.'

He looked, pathetically, like a child. What moral man could refuse? And the money would certainly come in handy.

I was still entirely convinced, of course, that Delaney was merely sleepwalking. It was an obvious conclusion. Well, if his foolishness was to line my pocket, so be it.

'What about the doll?' I asked.

He looked sickened at the mere mention of the thing.

'Lock it away. I will sell it the first chance I get.'

14.

SAFE-ROOM

THE DOLL *theme*

WILLIAMS: That evening, I did as I was asked; I locked the doll in one of Delaney's safe-rooms.

I returned it to its box; along with the papers. The only thing missing, of course, was the symbol that had been tied around its neck.

I stacked the box securely on a shelf and closed the re-enforced door as I left...

MUSIC stops

Distracted, suddenly.

...There are moments in life when one sees, say, a shadow on a wall, or a strange reflection in a mirror, and, at the time, the brain makes nothing of it. Because, of course, it is nothing.

A second or two later, however, memory shapes this shadow or reflection into something less innocent; more sinister. Often causing shivers to run down the spine.

I mention this because just after exiting the safe-room... I could have sworn that the shadow cast by the door in the torch light...

resembled a hunched figure, behaving in the manner of one who is hiding.

I checked the lock several times.

The lights drop. Williams turns on the torch and points it at the doll's box, which is securely closed.

15.

Williams sweeps the torchlight across the audience.

DELANEY'S ROOM

THE DOLL theme

WILLIAMS: Delaney's room was large and cold. The nest of blankets I had made for myself between the bed and the door was poor protection against the chill of the wooden floor. There had been no mention at all on Delaney's part that he might give up his bed for me. Heaven forfend!

I cursed my earlier fit of compassion. The whole situation was absurd. Were we school boys? Boy Scouts? At thirty-three years old, I was bunking with a man ten years my senior because he was frightened of a doll.

Torchlight comes to rest on the closed doll box.

Nevertheless, two nights of broken sleep meant that I slipped off quite quickly into a comfortable cocoon of slumber.

MUSIC fades

Torch off.

*

In darkness.

> It was still dark when I awoke; though I felt that I had slept for a long time.
>
> I could hear jagged and strained breathing coming from the bed. I flicked on my torch.

Williams flicks on torch light to illuminate own face.

> Delaney was sitting bolt upright, an expression of twisted revulsion on his face.
>
> There was another sound. Faint, but undoubtedly there and coming from near the door. Something was moving there. I followed Delaney's gaze and saw what had stricken him dumb.

The torch light moves to a trunk in the centre of the stage. The doll stands there, impossibly, facing the audience. In the torchlight - and just for a moment - we see its evil, eyeless face.

FX: *A PIERCING CRACK OF THUNDER, A FLASH OF LIGHTNING*

Williams cries out.

The torchlight returns to Williams' face.

WILLIAMS: Good God! The sight of the doll drove a cold shard of dread into my stomach; the thing had absolutely been locked away. I knew it had. Yet, there it was!

And - oh, dear God - *it was moving.* Its little head rocking from side to side, as a coy child might when engaged in play.

But the worst revelation was yet to come. Another look revealed something so monstrous, so uncannily repulsive that I believed, in that moment, I had gone quite mad:

MADNESS theme, quiet

The doll's movements were *not* happening of its own volition - something, I now saw, had hold of the thing's neck and was tilting it from side to side; something with long, pale fingers; something whose wrist revealed stretched, bleached flesh; something that was reaching through the crack in the door from the corridor outside...

Delaney let out a piercing shriek. This provoked that dreadful hand to snatch the doll out of the door.

There was silence for a moment... and then that deep, cruel laughter that I had heard in my dreams.

...and the door creaked open.

MADNESS theme, louder

The thing stood in the doorway, holding the doll.

My vision pulsed with the dread of it. It was tall and appallingly thin but with a powerful brawn about it.

And now it was coming into the room; taking strange, balletic steps forwards.

The pale thing thrust the doll violently at Delaney, as if challenging him to take it. When Delaney cried out, the rotten figure smiled in a most malignant way, revealing blackened teeth.

It reached out with its foul fingers, moving them in an appalling tickling motion.

It stepped over me, blocking my view of Delaney. But I knew that it must have laid its hands upon him... because he started to scream.

MUSIC stops

I'm ashamed of what I did next.

MUSIC - frantic stabs

I leapt up from the floor. And I fled the room.

In moments I was downstairs and out of the front door. As I started up the driveway, I tried to ignore the sounds of Delaney's screams still coming from the house.

I ran, as fast as I could, to Dorothy's cottage; leaving Delaney alone in the house... with that thing.

A HORROR IN PORCELAIN theme

16.

WILLIAMS: After my... escape, it was Dorothy who took control of the situation.

I had garbled my way through an explanation about an intruder in the house. I could not summon the truth, however hard I tried. I was not even sure what the truth of the matter was.

It couldn't be... It *couldn't* be...

DELANEY's theme

Dorothy called the authorities and, after a stiff drink to steady me, she convinced me to return with her to the house. She drove us back just as dawn began to break.

We saw the lights of the ambulance and the police cars from some distance away.

As we got to the front door, Delaney was being carried out of the house on a stretcher. I'll never forget that sight as long as I live. Nor the words that he spoke.

'I don't want to play!' he said. 'Give it the doll! I don't want it! Please, oh please, GOD! I don't want to play!'

MUSIC stops

The ambulance-men had tied a thick bandage across Delaney's face; hiding the bloodied places where his eyes had been.

I turned away from Delaney with that image seared onto my mind. Two police constables were making their way across the driveway towards me.

A HORROR IN PORCELAIN theme

EPILOGUE

STORYTELLER: And so there is little more to say. Mr Williams was incarcerated; that much is a matter of public record. But I could find no further details on what became of him. Nor of his employer. Perhaps it is better not to know.

The Storyteller stands, picks up the book.

As for us...

The Storyteller opens the book. There are many more tales left to tell.

We continue, onwards.

Sharing these dark tales until such a time as the book releases us.

He closes the book and moves as if to exit.

Turns to the audience, remembering something, and walks downstage.

I never told you how the book came to be in our possession...

FX: LATIN WHISPERS RISE TO A CRESCENDO

Well. That will have to be a tale for another night.

Blackout.

CURTAIN